SCOOBY-DOO! ™
Coloring & Activity Book

Bendon Publishing International, Inc.
Ashland, OH 44805
www.bendonpub.com

SCOOBY-DOO!™

...And A Mummy, Too!

"Anka vowed that if he were ever removed from his tomb,
he would turn those responsible to stone!"
"It'll take more than a curse to scare us off, Dr. Najib."

"Hey, Professor, like, what's with this crazy coin?"
"It's part of an ancient mystery I haven't been able to solve yet."
"Well, could you or Dr. Najib solve how I can
get a sandwich? I'm starving!"

HOW MANY WORDS CAN YOU MAKE OUT OF
VELMA DINKLEY?

1. KIND
5.
10.
15.
20.

COUNT THE WORDS
TO SEE WHOSE SEARCH
TEAM YOU'RE ON.

WORDS FOUND

1-5 SCOOBY'S TEAM

6-10 SHAGGY'S TEAM

11-15 DAPHNE'S TEAM

16-20 FRED'S TEAM

21 & UP VELMA'S TEAM

TM & © Hanna-Barbera.

"What kind of coin is this?"
"Whoa! I must've, like, dropped it in my pocket by accident."

The next day...
"The professor has turned to stone!"

Find THE IMPOSTER!

"Like… gulp… the mummy's gone, too."
"Interesting. The glass broke in, not out.
Looks like we have a mystery to solve."

In Search Of. . .

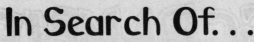

Help Freddy follow the footprints
to solve the mystery. You must find
12 footprints before you find the clue!
You cannot use the same path twice!

Start Here

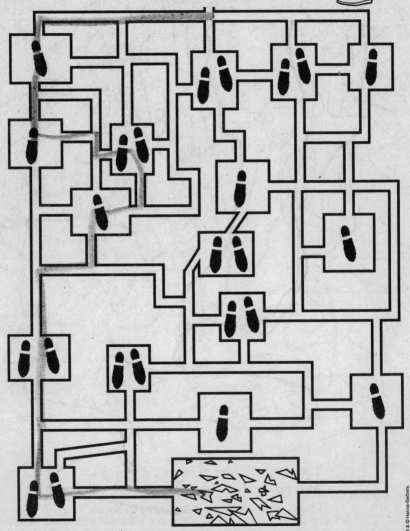

UNSCRAMBLE

What are Shaggy and Scooby making?
Unscramble the letters. The letters in the box will reveal the answer.

1. OYSPOK _ _ _ _ _ _

2. PIEVAMR _ _ _ _ _ _ _

3. NELNTAR _ _ _ _ _ _ _

4. NAHDEP _ _ _ _ _ _

5. HICWT _ _ _ _ _

6. IHEFT _ _ _ _ _

7. UCLE _ _ _ _

8. LGUSHO _ _ _ _ _ _

"Let's split up and find the mummy."

"Oh, no! Dr. Najib's turned to stone!
He must've run into the mummy."
"I wonder if the others have found him yet."

WHO'S SCARED?

Match Scooby-Doo to his correct shadow.

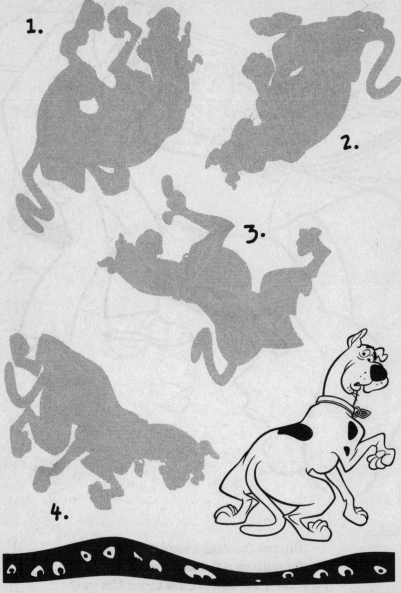

1.

2.

3.

4.

"Zoinks! That wasn't hard was it, Scoob?"
"COIN! COIN!"

"Lay some karate on him, Scooby!"
"Right! Rarate!"

DRAW A CONCLUSION
Who stole all of the Scooby Snacks?

To identify the thief, draw the contents of each box in the grid below.
Use the coordinates to locate the correct position of each piece.

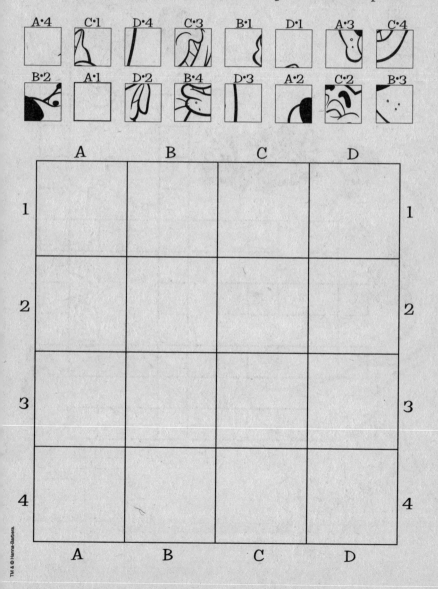

HAUNTED CROSSWORD

Fill in the words that correspond to the pictures.

"Oh, no!"

"My old pal. He's gone to that Big Boneyard in the Sky."

TM & © Hanna-Barbera.

"I don't get it."
"Let's go back to the professor's office.
Maybe we can dig up some answers to this mystery."

"Apparently, Anka was the richest pharaoh of ancient Egypt!"
"Now that's what I call a real riches to rags story.
Look out! Here comes Old Moldy himself."

Help Scooby and Shaggy find the Scooby Snacks without running into any ghouls.

"COIN! COIN!"
"Quick, Scoob! In here!"

"I've got an idea, Scoob."

"Look! There's Shag, Scoob, and the mummy, too!"

"Now let's see who's really behind these bandages!"
"DOCTOR NAJIB!"

SUPER SLEUTH

Scooby and the gang need a clue.
Fold the page forward at line A and back at line B so the edge meets line C.
You've uncovered a very important clue!

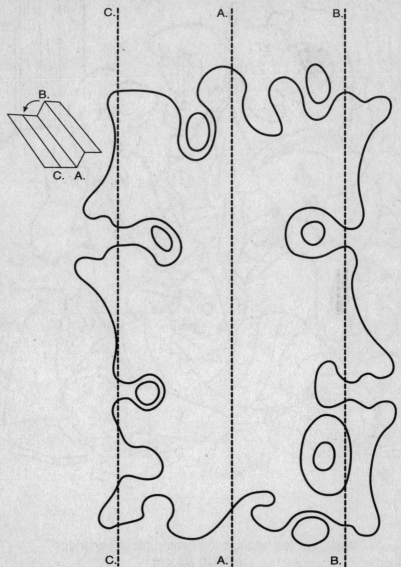

"So, it's apparent that Doctor Najib knew the secret of the coin, and disguised himself as the mummy to scare us into giving it to him."
"And I would have gotten away with it, if not for you meddling kids!"

Haunted House Hang-Up

"If we don't find some kind of road sign to tell us
which way to the concert, we're in trouble."

"I think we're into trouble already — look."
"Yikes!"
"Double Yikes!"

HOW MANY WORDS CAN YOU MAKE OUT OF

HAUNTED HOUSE?

1. HUNT

5.

10.

15.

20.

COUNT THE WORDS
TO SEE WHOSE SEARCH
TEAM YOU'RE ON.

WORDS FOUND

1-5 SCOOBY'S TEAM

6-10 SHAGGY'S TEAM

11-15 DAPHNE'S TEAM

16-20 FRED'S TEAM

21 & UP VELMA'S TEAM

**"I'm Asa Shanks. There's a headless specter up
at the old mansion, so you kids steer clear!"**

"Dang, the Mystery Machine's overheating! I saw a well back by that old mansion. Shag, you and Scoob go check it out."

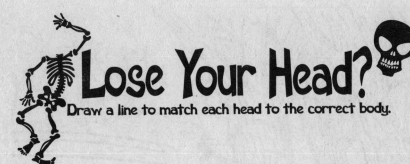

Lose Your Head?

Draw a line to match each head to the correct body.

"Ghosts!!!"

**"No water at the well, huh? There's a light on in the mansion.
See if you can get a bucket of water there."**

DRAW A CONCLUSION

Who ate all of the sandwiches?

To identify the thief, draw the contents of each box in the grid below.
Use the coordinates to locate the correct position of each piece.

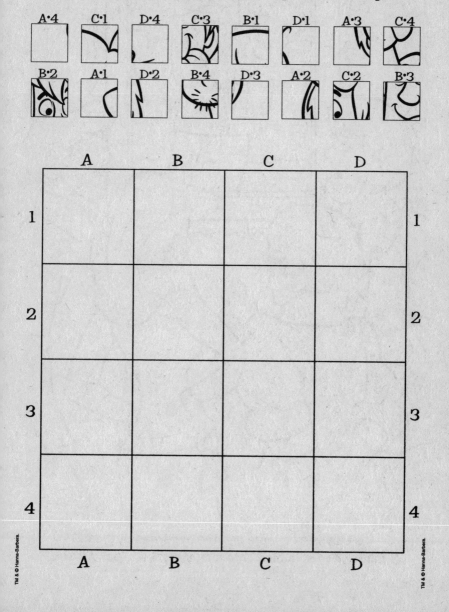

"L-L-Look! A minute ago the head was th-there."
"I think we've stumbled onto a mystery. Let's look around."

UNSCRAMBLE

What does Velma always exclaim?

Unscramble the letters. The letters in
the box will reveal the answer.

1. EWSJLE

2. LIAVNLI

3. DACLEN

4. YEK

5. ERMCI

6. AESURTRE

7. YSMETYR

ANSWERS: 1. JEWELS 2. VILLAIN 3. CANDLE 4. KEY 5. CRIME 6. TREASURE 7. MYSTERY

"This is just a wooden dummy. It was deliberately placed here to scare us."

"A clue!"
"Dig these crazy footprints!"
"Let's split up and follow 'em."

Help Scooby-Doo find Shaggy
without running into any ghouls.

Start

Finish

"Yikes! It's the headless specter!!!"

"Like, we lost him — and found a secret tunnel."
"It could lead to the solution to this whole mystery."

MAD SCIENTIST'S LABORATORY

Create your own monster.

"Stillwell Shows the Way. I've got it! Find the column Stillwell'
portrait is pointing out and we've solved the mystery."
"Let's find the others first."

Find THE IMPOSTER!

ANSWER: 2

"Hey, look at this, gang: balloons and helium."
"Jinkies! I think we're on to something."

"This sheet tossed over the helium balloon will float up.
Is this your ghost, guys?"
"Yep, and there's another! Run, Scoob!"

HAUNTED CROSSWORD

Fill in the words that correspond to the pictures.

ANSWER:

(Answer key, shown inverted:)

NOTELEKS (SKELETON)
TREASURE
HOUSE
SANDWICH
FOOTPRINTS
HAUNT
SHAGGY

"Hey, you guys! Help!!"

"Oh, my achin' head."
"Hey, you really have a head."

SUPER SLEUTH

Scooby and the gang need a clue.
Fold the page forward at line A and back at line B so the edge meets line C.
You've uncovered a very important clue!

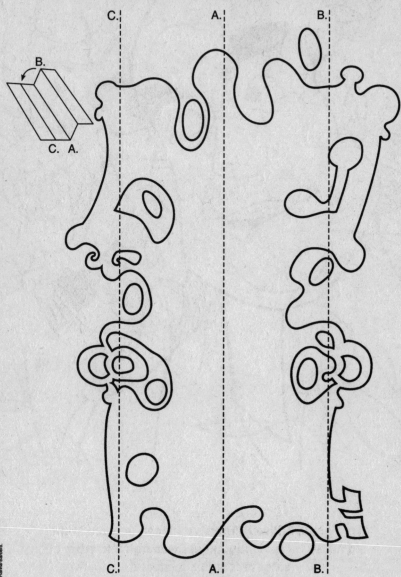

"I'm Penrod Stillwell. There's a hidden treasure in that old house that's rightly mine! I was trying to scare off whoever's trying to steal it."

"I've got a plan that'll rid us of that someone."

In Search Of...

Help Velma follow the footprints to solve the mystery. You must find 12 footprints before you find the clue! You cannot use the same path twice!

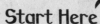

Start Here

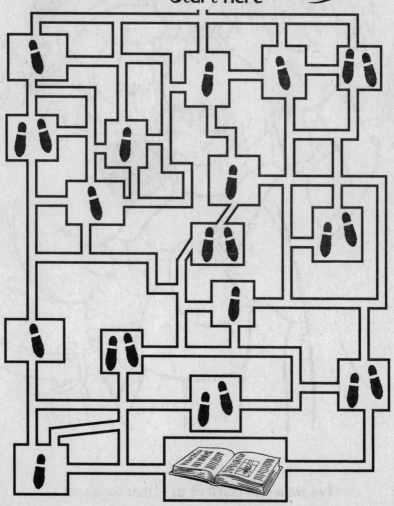

"He's right behind us."

"Let's see who this phony phantom really is."
"It's Asa Shanks!"